OCEANS

There is more ocean on our planet than there is land, but we still know little about it. The first ship sailed all the way around the world less than five hundred years ago. And the first journey to the deepest sea floor was little more than fifty years ago.

Great waves move across the surface of the ocean, and currents of cold and warm water move past our continents. The biggest animals on our planet swim around the Southern Ocean, and in the hottest parts of the ocean we can find animals that live without light. It is a strange world – and we are just beginning to know it . . .

OXFORD BOOKWORMS LIBRARY

Factfiles

Oceans

Stage 2 (700 headwords)

Factfiles Series Editor: Christine Lindop

BARNABY NEWBOLT

Oceans

OXFORD UNIVERSITY PRESS

OXFORD
UNIVERSITY PRESS

Great Clarendon Street, Oxford, OX2 6DP, United Kingdom

Oxford University Press is a department of the University of Oxford.
It furthers the University's objective of excellence in research, scholarship,
and education by publishing worldwide. Oxford is a registered trade
mark of Oxford University Press in the UK and in certain other countries

ISBN: 978 0 19 479443 5   Book
ISBN: 978 0 19 463778 7   Book and audio pack

Printed in China

Word count (main text): 6,778 words

For more information on the Oxford Bookworms Library,
visit www.oup.com/elt/gradedreaders

ACKNOWLEDGEMENTS

With thanks to: Ann Fullick for expert science advice

Cover by EXTREME-PHOTOGRAPHER courtesy of Getty Images/E+

Maps and diagrams by: Peter Bull pp. 3, 12, 13, 17, 23.

The publisher would like to thank the following for permission to reproduce photographs:
Alamy pp. 5 (ZUMA Press), 7 (North Wind Picture Archives), 9 (Vasco Da Gama/Ian G Dagnall),
10 (Martin Witte), 11 (North Wind Picture Archives), 15 (sea spider/Andrey Nekrasov),
19 (Comic sketch by T S Seacombe showing King Canute and his courtiers/Walker Art Library),
25 (robertharding), 26 (Bruce Miller); Ardea p. 16 (hagfish/Pat Morris); FLPA pp. 15 (starfish/
ImageBroker), 28 (Reinhard Dirschner), 33 (Hiroya Minakuchi/Minden Pictures), 36 (Norbert
Wu), 37 (Norbert Wu); Getty pp. 2 (Reed Kaestner/Corbis), 8 (Alison Wright/The Image Bank
Unreleased), 9 (map/DEA Picture Library/De Agostini Editorial), 18 (JIJI PRESS/AFP), 20 (James
Osmond/The Image Bank Unreleased), 27 (Bligh leaves the Bounty/Print Collector/Hulton
Archive), 32 (blue whale/richcarey/iStock), 39 (QAI Publishing/Universal Images Group); Nature
Picture Library pp. 16 (sleeper shark/Franco Banfi), 29 (Doug Perrine), 30 (Doug Perrine); Oxford
University Press pp. 0 (planet/Graphi-Ogre, starry sky/Photodisc), 44 (map/Graphi-Ogre, ice/
plastic forks/wave/compass/Photodisc, gas hob/Magelanic Cloud S); Science Photo Library
pp. 13 (topographic globe/Planetary Visions Ltd), 22 (low tide/high tide/Andrew J. Martinez),
32 (albatross/Tony Camacho), 34 (J. G. Paren), 40 (Dr Ken MacDonald).

CONTENTS

1   Planet Ocean

Look up into the sky at night, and you will see stars all around you – more stars than you can count. Many of these stars give light to other planets. But only one of all these planets – Planet Earth – has life on it. Why is this? We can put the answer in one word: water. If we look at our planet from a long way away, it is not yellow like the Sun, nor white like the Moon – it is blue. Blue is the colour of the oceans, and 72 per cent of the surface of our planet is ocean. Perhaps we should change the name of our planet from Planet Earth to Planet Ocean.

More animals live in the oceans than on the land. This is possible only because there is so much food in the oceans. Where does the food come from? As we shall see in Chapter Four, the 'first food' of our oceans is plants. If you take all the plants out of the oceans, very few animals can live there. To make their food, plants need water and sunlight. They also need minerals, and the minerals come from the land.

So life in the oceans is possible only with help from the land. But the opposite is also true: life on land is possible only with help from the oceans. We need water to live, and that comes to us from the oceans. Rain clouds take water from the oceans, and ocean winds carry the clouds over the land, where the rain falls onto our fields and into our rivers.

The oceans make our weather – but they also make our climate. Because of our oceans, our planet is neither too hot nor too cold. The waters of the oceans move around the world, bringing warm water to cold places and cold water to hot places. Life is possible everywhere on our planet because the water in our oceans is always moving. We will learn how this happens in Chapter Seven.

Of course, the oceans can also be dangerous. We are all afraid of storms at sea – and of the terrible waves of a tsunami. But for many of us, oceans are places of adventure, mystery, and hope. It is always exciting to climb into a boat. We do not know what we will find on the other side of the ocean, or in the deepest parts of the ocean – a hidden world until 150 years ago. But we want to try – we want to find new places and learn more about our world, just as the first ocean travellers did thousands of years ago.

2 Ocean people

Easter Island is a long way from anywhere. The nearest place to it is a very small island called Pitcairn, which is 2,250 kilometres to the west. Then there is Tahiti, which is 4,250 kilometres to the northwest, and Chile, which is 3,765 kilometres to the east. Easter Island is the most remote island in the Pacific, but people have lived there for about a thousand years! How did they get there? And where did they come from?

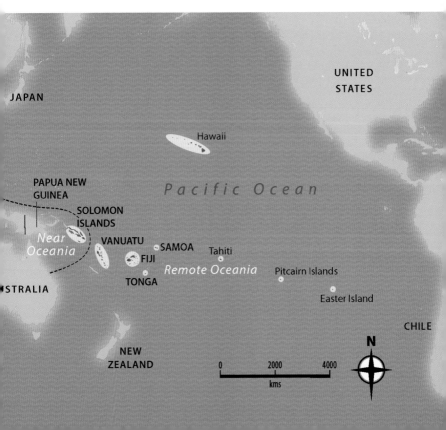

The earliest ocean travellers lived about 50,000 years ago. Their boats were small and they could not go far in them. But they did not have to go far. At the southeast corner of the Asian continent, the islands are near to the land, and it is easy to travel to them. The name for this group of islands is Near Oceania. These first ocean travellers went from island to island, making new homes for themselves. Then they arrived at Papua New Guinea and the Solomon Islands. That was as far as they could go. To go any further, they needed better boats – and they needed to learn how to sail.

Both of these things happened about 4,000 years ago. The Lapita (the early people of Polynesia) had large boats: ten to twenty people could live on them. They took food and water with them, but also animals and plants. They were looking for new islands – new places to make their homes. And they made long journeys of 800 kilometres or more across the open sea.

How did they do this? At this time, sea travellers on all the other oceans stayed near to the land – they needed to see the land to get back home. They did not have compasses to show the way, and there were no maps. But the Lapita did not need them.

The Lapita were the first 'ocean people'. They understood the ocean and were not afraid of it. They knew that the wind usually came from the southeast, but that at some times of year it changed and came from the northwest. They knew that when the waves were big, they were near land. They knew where to find fish and where to look for birds. And – most important of all –

A large Polynesian boat

they understood the stars and knew where to find them at different times of year. They were the first people to sail across the open ocean because they knew that they could come back. In other words, they learned to navigate.

The first long journeys of the Lapita were to the southeast. They arrived on Vanuatu, Fiji, Samoa, and Tonga – a group of islands we call Remote Oceania – about 3,000 years ago. They travelled southeast, using the winds from the northwest, because they knew that they could easily come back with the more usual southeasterly winds. They continued travelling, but the other islands of the South Pacific were much further away. They were either difficult to find, or difficult to live on – or both. The Lapita did not make homes on the furthest islands – Hawaii and Easter Island – until just over a thousand years ago. And it took them a few hundred years more to arrive in New Zealand, after they learned how to travel across the winds to the southwest.

We also think that, about a thousand years ago, the Lapita (we call them Polynesians at this date) went all the way across the Pacific, past Easter Island, to South America. We know that they brought back a plant with them – the sweet potato – and planted it on their islands. And, strangely, at about the same time, another group of people were crossing a different ocean – the Atlantic – and pulling their boats up onto the beaches of North America. These people came from Norway and Denmark, and they were famous for fighting, killing, and stealing. They were not looking for empty islands – they were looking for gold. These people were the Vikings.

3   Looking for gold

All over the world, sailors are famous for telling stories – which are not always true. One of the most famous storytellers, Sinbad the Sailor, tells the stories of his adventures at sea in the book *Arabian Nights*. At the beginning of each adventure, Sinbad is bored with life at home and decides to go on a sea journey. In each story, he loses his ship – usually in a storm – and the sea carries him to a strange and wonderful land. There are many dangers for him: perhaps he has to fight strange animals or terrible monsters from the sea.

Sinbad loses his ship

But he is never afraid. He kills the monsters, finds bags of gold, and sails home in a new ship as a rich man.

Stories about sea adventures are the same all over the world. People have always thought that a rich future was waiting for them somewhere across the oceans. Some hoped to be lucky, like Sinbad, and find bags of gold waiting for them on a remote island. Others used their ships to take villages by surprise, arriving early in the morning or late at night, and then killing, burning, and

A Viking longship

stealing. This is what the Vikings did a thousand years ago. Their long, narrow boats – called longships – were better and faster than any other boats. For two hundred years, the North Atlantic belonged to them. Nobody could stop them. You could not ask them to go away; you had to pay them to go away – with lots of gold.

This is because the Vikings were business people too. They had other ships which were bigger and wider, and they used them to travel to countries as far away as Russia and Turkey. They went there to trade, to buy and sell. They sold wood and fish, and bought silver and glass – but they also bought and sold people. These people were slaves – they belonged to and worked for others for no money. The Vikings were not the first people to trade in slaves, and they were not the last. But they taught the rest of the world an important lesson: ships were the future. To be rich and important, from now on countries needed good, strong, fast ships.

International trade – trade between different countries – was much easier with ships. For hundreds of years, a lot of the trade between Asia and Europe had to go over the land. But in 1498 a Portuguese sailor, Vasco da Gama, sailed around the south of Africa for the first time, arriving in the Indian Ocean and opening the eastern sea road to Asia. Six years before this, in 1492, Christopher Columbus (an Italian sailor in a Spanish ship) tried to find the western sea road to Asia. He did not get to the Pacific Ocean, because there was land in the way, but he was one of the first Europeans to visit the Americas. The first person to find the western sea road into the Pacific was another Portuguese sailor, Ferdinand Magellan. In 1522, his ship *Victoria* was the first ship to sail all the way around

Vasco da Gama, and a map of the world in his time

the world. International trade was ready to begin. The world was open for business.

Today, people make international business journeys in aeroplanes, but ships are more important than ever for moving things around the world. Modern ships carry things in large metal boxes called containers. Each container is about six metres long – and they say that one container can hold 48,000 bananas! The largest container ship in the world, the *Emma Maersk*, is about 400 metres long and can carry 11,000 containers – that is 528 million bananas!

Because of modern ships, international trade is faster and better. Is it the same for the fishing business? Modern

The *Emma Maersk*

Opposite page: Catching
cod in Newfoundland

fishing ships are very good at finding and catching fish, but perhaps they are too good. In 1497, John Cabot (an Italian sailor in an English ship this time), sailed west across the Atlantic. He was hoping to find new lands, like Christopher Columbus five years before him.

He found new land – the place now called Newfoundland – but he also found fish. At a place near the coast of Newfoundland, called the Grand Banks, the sea is not very deep. When Cabot arrived there, the water was full of fish. These fish were called cod, and everyone in the world wanted cod. It was like finding gold. For hundreds of years after this, fishermen came to the Grand Banks to catch cod. But in 1992, the cod fishing stopped. There were not enough fish.

The story of Newfoundland cod is an important lesson for us. It is stupid to think that there are bags of gold waiting for us on remote islands. It is stupid to think that there is no end to the fish in the sea. Before we take things, we must understand what we are doing. How much do we really understand about the oceans? To answer that, we first need to ask the question: what is the ocean? Perhaps the answer will surprise you.

4   What is the ocean?

Many people think that an ocean is land with lots of sea over it. In fact, the land of our continents is made of a different rock from the land under our oceans. Oceanic rock is made of basalt; continental rock is made of granite. Here are two interesting things: firstly, basalt is much heavier than granite; and secondly, the basalt under our oceans is much younger (around two billion years younger!) than the granite under our continents.

Our planet is like a ball that is made in three pieces. At the centre of the ball, deep inside the Earth, is the core. Around the Earth's core is the mantle. And around

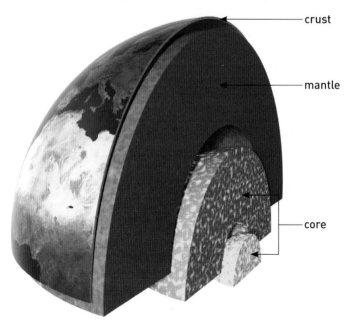

crust

mantle

core

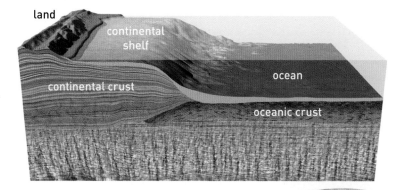

land
continental
shelf
continental crust
ocean
oceanic crust

the Earth's mantle is the crust, the surface of the planet. Now, the crust is hard – it is made of rock (either basalt or granite). But the mantle, underneath the crust, is soft and very hot – like a sea of fire. The Earth's crust floats on the mantle like a boat floats on water. But basalt is heavier than granite, so the basalt crust sinks more deeply into the mantle than the granite crust. That is why our continents are higher than our oceans.

But there is a lot of water in the oceans, and in some places it comes up over the continental crust. If you have swum in the sea, you will know this. When you walk from the beach into the sea, the water is not deep immediately. You are walking on – and swimming over – continental crust, not oceanic crust. This is called a continental shelf. Most continental shelves go out to sea for many kilometres: the Siberian Shelf goes out for 1,500 kilometres. But the coasts of Chile and West Sumatra have no shelves at all.

The waters over our continental shelves are home to most of the animals and plants that live in the sea. Firstly, this is because these waters are not deep. Sunlight does not get much further than 200 metres below the surface of the water. As we saw in Chapter One, plants need sunlight, and animals need plants. And secondly, there are plenty of minerals here. Plants need minerals to grow, and the land of the continental crust is rich in minerals – much richer than the oceanic crust. Rivers and rain wash these minerals – and lots of other things – out of the land and into the sea.

With sunlight and minerals, billions of small plants can grow in these waters. These small plants are called phytoplankton (the word means 'floating plants'). Without them, there could be no life in our oceans. Phytoplankton are food for small animals called zooplankton (floating animals) and for small fish. And these small animals are food for everything else.

But some of this food from the land sinks into deep water. Sea currents carry the food further out to sea. Because of these currents, life is possible almost everywhere in our oceans. We will learn about currents in Chapter Seven.

The water of the seas and oceans is salty. When the water gets warm, it goes into clouds in the sky. When it gets very cold, it changes into ice. But the salt does not go into the clouds or the ice – it stays in the sea. And that is why our oceans are always salty.

5   The ocean floor

When you leave the continental shelf, the ocean is suddenly very deep. Behind you, the waters were full of life and the sea floor was only 200 or 300 metres below. Now, the waters around you are empty, and the ocean floor is more than 2,000 metres below. It is dark here too. If you go down more than 200 metres, light from the sun will not follow you.

If you take a light down with you, you will see that the ocean floor is grey – almost without colour. It is like a soft carpet, hundreds of metres deep, over the oceanic rock. This carpet, called globigerina ooze, is made of the shells of millions of dead sea animals. Most of the ocean floor has ooze like this over it. What could possibly live in a place like this?

But things do live here. Sea spiders and starfish move slowly over the ooze, looking for little pieces of dead fish that have sunk down from the surface. And if a larger

A sea spider (below) and a starfish

A sleeper shark (above)
and a hagfish

meal comes down – the body of a whale, for example – then the larger fish arrive. Sleeper sharks swim slowly: there is no hurry, because this food will not escape. Hagfish are always in a hurry. They want to get inside the body of the whale, where the food is soft.

Underneath the carpet of ooze is rock, the oceanic crust, made of basalt. It is much younger than the crust under our continents. Why is this?

The Earth's crust floats on the mantle underneath it. But the crust is not made of one piece – it is made of seven large pieces, and many smaller ones. These are called tectonic plates (building plates), and they are always moving. They move very slowly, but everything on the surface of the planet moves with them.

When two plates come together, two things can happen. Sometimes one of the plates pushes the other plate back down into the mantle. When this happens, a trench (a long, deep hole) is made. The Mariana Trench, nearly 11,000 metres below the surface of the Pacific Ocean, is the deepest of our trenches, and the deepest hole in our planet. But sometimes one of the plates pushes the other plate up into the sky. This is how our tallest mountains, the Himalayas, were made.

When two plates move away from each other, they leave a hole. New rock, soft and very hot, comes up from the mantle through this hole. The new rock makes either a seamount (an underwater mountain) or a ridge (a long hill) of new oceanic crust. This is how the Mid-Atlantic Ridge was made. This underwater mountain ridge runs all the way under the Atlantic Ocean from Iceland to the Antarctic. The islands of Iceland and the Azores are the tops of this ridge: places where the ridge is higher than the sea around it.

Our planet is about 4.5 billion years old. Not so long ago – only 200 million years ago – there was only one large continent, called Pangaea, and one large ocean around it. The Atlantic Ocean was no more than a large river.

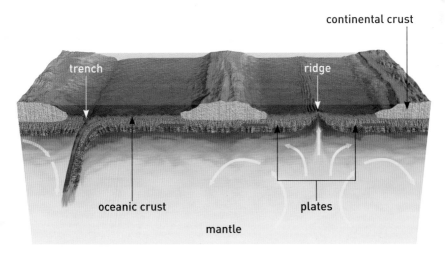

The tsunami in Japan, 2011

But the plates under the Atlantic – two in the north, and two in the south – started to move away from each other. Each year they moved 2.5 centimetres further away, and 2.5 centimetres of new oceanic crust was made. And the same thing is happening now under our oceans. In one place, old crust is sinking into the Earth's mantle, and in another place, hot rock is coming up to make new crust.

Tectonic plates usually move very slowly, and we do not feel them moving. But when they move suddenly, they make earthquakes. If an earthquake happens under the ocean, it makes a tsunami. This happened on 11 March 2011. Two plates moved suddenly at the Japan Trench. It was Japan's largest earthquake, and its worst tsunami, and it killed many thousands of people. Honshu, the largest island of Japan, moved 2.5 metres to the east.

6   The tides

There is a famous story about King Cnut, a Viking king of England long ago. Cnut's people thought that he was wonderful, and they told him so all the time. They said that he could do anything – even stop the sea from moving. Cnut was tired of this talk. He carried his seat to the beach and stood with the sea in front of him.

'Stop! Go back, sea!' he shouted – but the sea came up over his feet. Cnut turned to his people. 'Everyone must learn from this,' he said. 'No man on earth can stop the sea.'

Cnut tells the sea to stop

The sea never stops moving. Twice a day, the sea comes up. For six hours and twelve minutes, it gets higher – and then it starts to go down again. After another six hours and twelve minutes, it is ready to come up for the second time. Why does this happen? It is because of the Moon, of course. The Earth needs twenty-four hours to turn round once and get back to its starting place with the Sun – we call this a solar (Sun) day. But the Moon is moving around the Earth, so the Earth needs a little longer to get back to its starting place with the Moon. This takes twenty-four hours and forty-eight minutes, and we call it a lunar (Moon) day.

As the Moon moves around the Earth, it pulls the oceans with it. This is called gravity. The Moon's gravity makes two waves – one on the side of the Earth nearest to it, and one on the side furthest from it. Because the Earth is turning to the east, the waves travel to the west. These two waves are the two high tides that move up our beaches each day. The Sun's gravity pulls the oceans, too; but because the Sun is much further away, it does not pull so strongly. When the Moon and the Sun pull together (every two weeks), the tides are bigger; when they pull against each other, the tides are smaller.

Low tide in St Ives, England

Low tide   **High tide**

In some places, the tides are very small. This happens when land gets in the way of the tide, for example in the Mediterranean Sea and the Gulf of Mexico. But in other places, the tides can be very large; in other words, in the six hours and twelve minutes from high tide to low tide, the sea moves down a long way. In the Bay of Fundy, for example, in the east of Canada, the sea is sometimes sixteen metres higher at high tide than it is at low tide on the same day.

Big tides like these move a lot of water. When the tide comes in, it washes the land, and brings food up into the sea. Fish often come in with the tide, so it is a good time to take your fishing rod to the beach. And when the tide goes out, it takes minerals, plankton (those small plants and animals), and other food away from the land, and out into the deeper ocean. Here, the big ocean currents will take them on a journey all the way around the world. That is what we will look at in the next chapter.

7   Ocean currents

When the wind moves over the sea, it pushes the surface of the water and moves it like a river. When the water moves like this, it is called a surface current. Strong winds can move water as far down as 100 metres below the surface.

Near to the land, the winds change from day to day, and the currents change with the wind. Or, if the sea is not deep, the currents follow the land underneath them, just like a river. But further out on the open ocean, the winds and currents stay the same for most of the year. They move in large circles, called gyres. There are five large gyres in our oceans: two in the Pacific, two in the

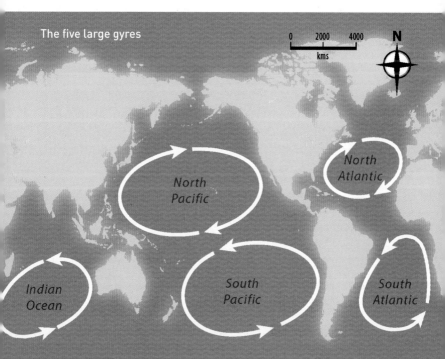

The five large gyres

North Pacific

North Atlantic

Indian Ocean

South Pacific

South Atlantic

Atlantic, and one in the Indian Ocean. In the northern oceans, the gyres turn clockwise (the same way as the hands of a clock). In the southern oceans, they turn anti-clockwise (the opposite way from the hands of a clock). The winds move in gyres because the Earth is turning. The winds try to go in a straight line – from the cold top or bottom of the Earth to the hot middle, and back again. But the turning Earth spins the winds, so that they move in gyres.

It is sometimes difficult to escape from the currents in these gyres. People have seen large 'islands' of very small pieces of plastic that are floating just below the surface in the middle of our oceans. The largest of these is in the North Pacific Gyre.

The Gulf Stream is a strong, warm current on the western side of the North Atlantic Gyre. It moves from the Gulf of Mexico past the east of the United States, and then it moves across to Europe. The climate of northwest Europe is warmer than other northern places because of the warm waters of the Gulf Stream.

But not all the water of the Gulf Stream follows the gyre clockwise around the North Atlantic. Some of it goes north past the United Kingdom and up to the Arctic Ocean. This is a very cold place, and when the current arrives here, some of the water freezes (changes into ice). But the salt in the water cannot freeze, so it stays in the sea. This seawater is now saltier and heavier than the water around it, so it sinks to the ocean floor. It cannot stay there because more cold and heavy water is coming down on top of it. So it begins to move south along the

ocean floor. It is starting a long journey that will carry it
right around the world in deep ocean currents.

The journey starts in the Arctic. The deep ocean
current moves south along the continents of North and
South America, following the ocean floor like a river. At
the bottom of South America, it cannot turn west into the
Pacific, as there is an underwater ridge that stops it, so it
turns east along the icy continent of Antarctica. Here it
meets more cold, heavy water that is sinking down off
the ice. Now there are two currents: one moving north
into the Indian Ocean, and one going east around the
bottom of the world – the long way into the Pacific. The
currents move north until they meet land. The water that
is coming behind them pushes them up to the surface.
Now they are warm, and they begin their journey home.
They move south to the Southern Ocean, and then turn
north into the Atlantic, going back to the place where
they began.

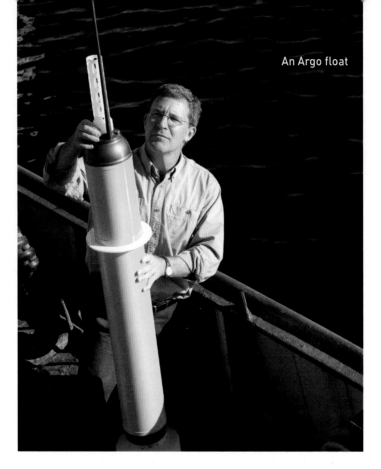
An Argo float

Deep ocean currents do a very important thing. They move water from the top of the ocean to the bottom and back again, bringing minerals, plankton, and other food to the most remote places in our oceans. We think that the journey around the world takes more than a thousand years, but we are still learning about it. At this moment, while you are reading these words, three thousand small computers, called Argo floats, are floating one kilometre below the surface of our oceans. Deep ocean currents are carrying them on their long journeys. Every ten days, the computers come up to the surface to tell us where they are. Then they sink, going back to their lonely journeys around the oceans of the world.

8   The open ocean

On the night of 28 April 1789, a ship was travelling in the South Pacific, in the lonely waters of Remote Oceania. The ship's captain, William Bligh, was sleeping in his room when some sailors came in with guns. The sailors did not like the captain and wanted to take the ship, *HMS Bounty*, for themselves. They put Bligh in a seven-metre boat, with eighteen other men who wanted to stay with him, and they left them on the open ocean. The sailors took the *Bounty* to the remote island of Pitcairn, where they burned it. Families of these sailors still live on the island today.

Bligh leaves the *Bounty*

What happened to Captain Bligh? The sailors gave him a compass, but not a map. Luckily, he was a good navigator. Using the compass and the stars in the sky, he sailed the small boat, with all the other men, nearly 7,000 kilometres across the Pacific to Timor, Indonesia. Their journey – in a boat that was open to the sun, wind, and rain – took forty-seven days.

The open ocean is an empty place – empty sky and empty sea. The fish that live here are large and very quick. They have to be quick, either to catch a smaller fish or to escape from a larger one. The sailfish, which is about 3 metres long, can swim at speeds of up to 110 kilometres per hour. It opens the large sail on its back to go faster, and to surprise other fish, by suddenly getting bigger in front of them. It also surprises other fish by changing colour: when a sailfish is excited, its body goes blue with yellow lines along it.

Sailfish

A great white shark

Most people are afraid of sharks. With their long, thin bodies, their small eyes, and their sharp teeth, they are made to be killers. The great white shark has three rows of teeth, one behind the other – about 300 teeth in all! If a shark loses a tooth, a new one moves into place from the row behind. Great whites can also move their teeth – a bit like fingers – to hold their food better after they have caught it! They have good noses, too, and can smell blood in the water from a long way away – as far as 5 kilometres. When you touch a great white shark's nose, it goes very still for a short time. Do not try this when they are hungry!

Finding food in the open ocean is difficult. The waters are empty most of the time. The best places to look are the currents that carry plankton with them – that is where the fish will be. The surface currents move around the oceans in gyres. But the deep currents bring food with them too. When the deep currents meet land, the land pushes them up to the surface. This is why there are so many fish around islands and seamounts. (We think there are over 100,000 seamounts in our oceans.)

Islands and seamounts are good places for small fish to hide. But there is nowhere to hide in the open ocean. What can small fish do when larger fish find them there? If the small fish cannot escape, they swim around each other very quickly in a small circle, making a ball of fish. At first, the larger fish are surprised – they do not know what to do. But after a minute or two, the surprise has gone, and the big fish begin their attack. Soon they break the ball into smaller pieces, and the fish are easier to catch. In ten minutes or so, the ball has gone. The big fish have finished their meal, and the sea is empty again – or nearly empty. There are some small pieces of dead fish that sink slowly down into the dark waters of the ocean floor. In an hour or two, the sea spiders and starfish will get their meal too.

Dolphins attack a ball of fish

9 The frozen oceans

At the bottom of the world lies the frozen continent of Antarctica. It is larger than Europe, but it is home to nobody, and the land belongs to no one. It is the coldest, windiest place on our planet. Nearly 90 per cent of the world's ice is here, and it goes far out over the sea, making tall shelves of ice above the water.

The Southern Ocean makes a circle around Antarctica. Some people say that it is not an ocean at all, but that it is the southern end of the Pacific, the Atlantic, and the Indian Oceans. But in 2000, the Southern Ocean was named as the world's fifth ocean (the Arctic Ocean is the fourth). Strong winds travel across the Southern Ocean, from west to east, making a current that moves in a circle around the Antarctic. Because of this, the ocean's waters stay colder than the waters to the north.

One family of birds has learned to use this wind very well. The albatross has the longest wings of any bird; on the biggest birds it is 3.4 metres or more from the end of one wing to the end of the other. It spends most of its life at sea, and only comes to land to rest and to have its young. It can travel hundreds of miles without resting because of how it flies. The albatross does not move its wings up and down very much; most of the time it keeps its wings still and uses them like a sail. It can 'lock' its wings so that it does not get tired when it does this.

An albatross

And it does not need to visit land often because it drinks seawater – keeping the water and pushing the salt out below its eyes.

Below the albatross, in the deep waters of the Southern Ocean, you can find the largest animal that has ever lived on our planet. The blue whale is 25 to 30 metres long. Its mouth can hold 90,000 kilograms of food and water – but it eats only very small animals, 1 to 2 centimetres long, called krill. In one day, it can eat over 3,000 kilograms of krill. This large animal has only two enemies, and the first of these is us. We have caught and killed blue whales for just over a hundred years. Today there are only about 10,000 of them still living in our oceans – that is under 5 per cent of the number living before that time.

A blue whale

The other animal that sometimes attacks the blue whale is the orca, also called the killer whale. This is a good name: they are very dangerous, and very clever, and they often work together in groups. They can even come out of the water to make a kill. People have seen orcas swimming up onto a beach to catch a seal. When seals are in danger from orcas, they sometimes climb out of

An orca tries to make a kill

the water onto a piece of ice to try to escape from them. When this happens, the orcas come together in a group and swim towards the ice in a line. This makes a wave that knocks the seal off the ice and back into the water, where the orcas can kill and eat it.

The frozen oceans are places that we do not visit very often, but they have been in the news a lot in the last few years. This is because their ice is melting. Our climate is changing.

We have a lot to learn about climate change. We know that it is happening, but we do not know how fast it is happening. Each summer, in the Antarctic, large pieces fall off the ice shelves over the sea, and float away. We call these icebergs. But in 2002, something very surprising happened. It was not an iceberg that fell into the sea – it was the shelf itself. The Larsen B Ice Shelf, 3,250 square kilometres of ice, fell into the sea – and it put the frozen oceans, and climate change, onto the front pages of our newspapers again.

The ice is possibly melting even more quickly in the north. The Arctic is an ocean that freezes every winter, but each year there is less ice both on the sea and on the land. Most of Greenland has ice over it. If all the ice on

An Antarctic iceberg

Greenland melts, the sea will be seven metres higher than it is today.

But perhaps this will not happen – and melting ice is not always a bad thing. The Siberian Shelf, which goes out into the Arctic Ocean for 1,500 kilometres, is rich with minerals like oil and gas. For thousands of years, the waters above it were frozen. But now the ice is melting, and soon it will be possible to get the minerals. So, who do they belong to? Is the continental shelf sea, or is it land? If the answer is sea, then the minerals belong to no one. If the answer is land, then perhaps the minerals belong to the country that is nearest to them. The countries that get the minerals will be very rich. The frozen oceans will stay in the news for a long time.

10 The deep ocean

The first ocean travellers pushed their boats into the sea 50,000 years ago. The Polynesians, and the Vikings, made the first ocean crossings 1,000 years ago. But our first journey to the bottom of the ocean happened only fifty years ago. The deep ocean – ocean that is more than a kilometre deep – is the largest place on our planet where life is possible. But we have only just started to learn about it.

The deep ocean is dark and cold. No light gets here from the sun, but there is some light – and it comes from the fish. The anglerfish is one of the monsters of the deep ocean. It has a large mouth and long, sharp teeth – and it

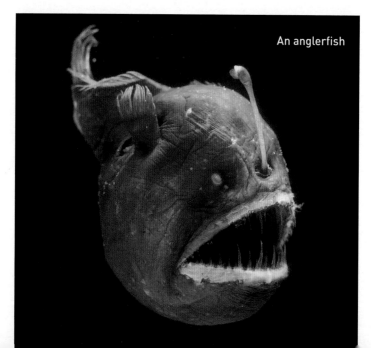

An anglerfish

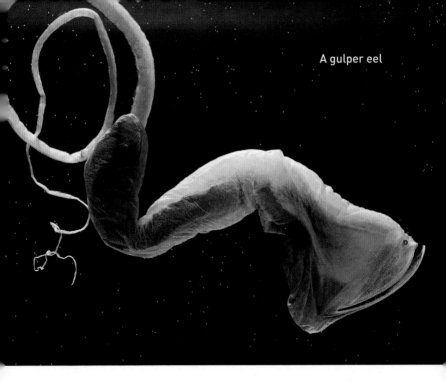

A gulper eel

has a 'fishing rod' growing out of its head! The rod has a light at the end of it. When other fish see the light, they are interested. They swim over to see what is happening, and before they know it – they are in the mouth of the anglerfish.

Down here, fish need large mouths: food is difficult to find. If something comes near to you, you have to eat it – sometimes even if it is bigger than you. This is what the gulper eel does. Its mouth is already larger than the rest of its body, but it can 'unlock' the bottom of its mouth to make it even bigger.

We do not know much about the deep ocean because it is difficult to get there. It is easier to build a boat to go on the water than under the water. The first underwater boat was built in 1620, in London, by a Dutchman called Cornelius Drebbel. It only went four or five metres below the surface of the water. This was not very deep; but in those days, nobody wanted to go very deep. They thought that there was nothing interesting down there.

Then in 1866, ships put a telegraph cable along the floor of the Atlantic Ocean. It was now possible to send eight words a minute between the UK and the USA! People were interested in the ocean floor and wanted to know more about it. So, in 1872, a ship called the *Challenger* began a three-year journey around the world. It made the first maps of the ridges and trenches across the ocean floor. (The Challenger Deep, the deepest place in the Mariana Trench, is named after this ship.) It also found nearly five thousand new sea animals and plants. For the first time, people learned that there was life in the deep ocean.

But they still could not get down there. More than sixty years later, in 1934, William Beebe and Otis Barton went down to 923 metres for the first time. And it was only in 1960 that Jacques Piccard went all the way down – 10,911 metres – to the bottom of the Challenger Deep.

Piccard's boat, the *Trieste*, could travel down to the ocean floor, but it could not move around. Another boat, the *Alvin*, was built a few years later. It could not go as deep, but it could move around more easily. On one of its early journeys, a very large fish attacked it. The *Alvin* was stronger than the fish: the boat lived, the fish died, and the sailors on the *Alvin* had it for their dinner.

In 1977, the *Alvin* was looking at the ocean floor in the East Pacific near the Galapagos Islands. People on the boat saw black smoke coming out of holes in the ground. They were looking at hydrothermal vents (hot water holes). These are holes in the ocean's crust where

The *Alvin* explores the ocean floor

hot, melted rock is coming through from the mantle. But it was not the vents that surprised people on the *Alvin*; it was the animals that were living around the vents. There were so many of them! Until that day, people thought that life was not possible this far from the light of the sun, and with so little food. There were lots of giant tube worms, which are red and white and can grow to more than 2 metres long. They do not need sunlight, or fish, or plants to stay alive; they get minerals from the hot water coming from the vents.

Now we know that many animals can live near to hydrothermal vents. One of these, a snail called *Crysomallon squamiferum*, has a shell with metal in it. Another, the Pompeii worm, can live in water as hot as 80 °C! These are like animals from another planet.

And that is what is interesting. We think that there are hydrothermal vents on other planets: perhaps on Mars and on Europa, one of the moons of Jupiter. If life is possible at the bottom of the ocean, then perhaps it is possible on other planets. Life began in our oceans: that is where we came from. Has life started at the bottom of another ocean, on another planet, perhaps not so far away?

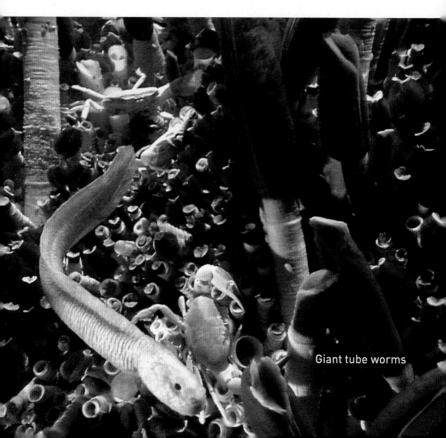

Giant tube worms

GLOSSARY

attack to try to hurt or kill someone

basalt a kind of dark rock that comes from volcanoes

captain the person in charge of a ship

climate the normal weather conditions of a place

coast the part of the land that is next to the sea

compass a thing for finding direction, with a needle that always points north

continent a very large piece of land, for example Africa; (*adj*) **continental**

current water that is moving

Earth the world; the planet that we live on

earthquake a sudden strong shaking of the ground

fishing rod a long thin stick with a thin thread and a hook, used for catching fish

float to stay on top of a liquid

freeze to become hard and turn to ice because of the cold; (*adj*) **frozen**

gas something like air (not solid or liquid) that we burn to make heat

granite a kind of hard grey rock

gravity a kind of force that pulls things towards each other or towards the ground

grow to get bigger; (of a plant) to exist in a particular place

ice water that has become hard because it is frozen

iceberg a very big piece of ice in the sea

king the most important man in a country

land the part of the Earth that is not the sea

line a long thin mark like this _____

map a drawing of a country or the world that shows things like mountains, rivers and seas

melt to become liquid after becoming warmer

metal something solid that is usually hard and shiny; iron and gold are metals

mineral something like coal, gold, or salt, that comes from the ground and that people use

monster an animal in stories that is big and frightening

oceanic belonging to the oceans

oil a thick liquid from under the ground that we use for energy

planet a large object in space that moves round the Sun; Earth and Venus are planets

plant (*n & v*) something that grows in the ground or in water; to put a plant in the ground

plastic an artificial material that is used for making many different things

remote far away from where other people live

rock something very hard that is found in the ground

sharp with a point that cuts easily

shell the hard outside part of some animals

sink to go down under water

spin to turn round and round

surface the top part of something

telegraph cable a wire that carries messages over long distances using electricity

tide the way that the sea goes up and down every day; **low tide** the time when the sea is furthest from the land

tsunami a very large wave caused by an earthquake

wave a line of water moving across the sea

whale a very large animal that lives in the sea

Oceans

ACTIVITIES

ACTIVITIES

Before Reading

1 **Match the words to the pictures. You can use a dictionary.**

1 ☐ plastic   3 ☐ compass   5 ☐ map

2 ☐ gas   4 ☐ ice   6 ☐ wave

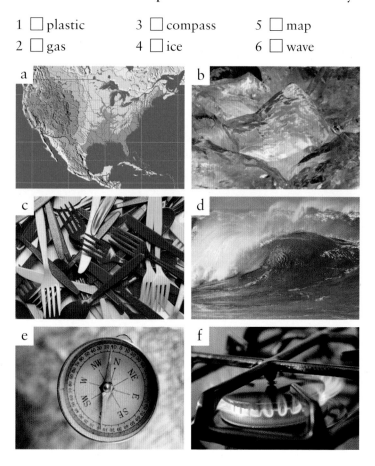

2 **All the words in Question 1 are used in *Oceans*. Can you guess why they are in the book? Make sentences about the world's oceans using these words.**

ACTIVITIES

While Reading

Read Chapter 1. Are these sentences true (T) or false (F)?

1 We cannot count all the stars in the sky.
2 There are many other planets.
3 If we look at Earth from a long way away, it is white.
4 Most of the surface of our planet is water.
5 More animals live on the land than in the oceans.
6 Plants need water and sunlight.
7 The water that we need comes from the oceans.

Read Chapter 2, then match these halves of sentences.

1 People have lived on Easter Island . . .
2 The first ocean travellers went . . .
3 The earliest ocean travellers did not have . . .
4 The Lapita were . . .
5 About a thousand years ago, the Lapita sailed . . .
6 The Vikings sailed . . .
7 The Vikings were famous for . . .

a from Asia to South America.
b compasses or maps.
c for about a thousand years.
d across the Atlantic Ocean.
e the first 'ocean people'.
f fighting, killing, and stealing.
g from island to island.

Read Chapter 3. Choose the best question words for these questions, and then answer them.

What / Where / Why

1 . . . did Sinbad the Sailor often decide to go on sea journeys?
2 . . . did Sinbad usually find on his journeys?
3 . . . were the Vikings' boats called?
4 . . . did the Vikings travel to Russia and Turkey?
5 . . . did Christopher Columbus come from?
6 . . . did Vasco da Gama sail for the first time?
7 . . . did cod fishing stop in 1992?

Read Chapters 4 and 5. Fill in the gaps with these words.

carpet, clouds, continental, core, crust, earthquake, grey, mantle, plates, salty, shells, sunlight

1 Our planet is like a ball that is made in three pieces. At the centre of the ball is the _____. Around this is the _____. The surface of the planet is the _____.
2 The waters over the _____ shelves are home to most of the animals and plants that live in the sea. These waters are not deep, so plants can get the _____ they need.
3 The water in the sea is _____. When the water gets warm, it goes into _____ in the sky, but the salt stays in the sea.
4 The ocean floor is _____, almost without colour. It is like a soft _____, and is made of the _____ of millions of dead sea animals.
5 The Earth's crust is made of tectonic _____. When these move suddenly, they can make an _____.

Read Chapters 6 and 7, then rewrite these untrue sentences with the correct information.

1 King Cnut wanted to show that he could stop the sea.
2 Tides happen because of the stars.
3 The Earth needs twenty-four days to turn round once and get back to its starting place with the Sun.
4 The tides are very large in the Mediterranean Sea.
5 Winds move in gyres because the Moon is turning.
6 Northwest Africa is warmer than other northern places because of the Gulf Stream.
7 Seawater that is very cold and salty floats to the top of the ocean.
8 Argo floats are small boats that travel around the world.

Read Chapter 8. Circle the correct words.

1 Sailors came into Captain Bligh's room with *fishing rods / guns*.
2 The sailors took the *HMS Bounty* to the remote *island / continent* of Pitcairn.
3 The sailors gave Bligh a *map / compass* for his journey.
4 Bligh sailed nearly *700 / 7,000* kilometres across the ocean.
5 The *sailfish / great white shark* can swim at 110 kilometres per hour.
6 The great white shark has about *300 / 3,000* teeth.

Before you read Chapter 9, think about the chapter title, *The frozen oceans*. Which places do you think you will read about? What do you know about these places? Are they important? Do any people or animals live there?

Read Chapter 9. Circle *a*, *b*, or *c*.

1 Antarctica is _____ Europe.
  a) smaller than   b) the same size as   c) bigger than

2 Nearly 90 per cent of the world's ice is in _____.
  a) Antarctica   b) the Arctic Ocean   c) Greenland

3 The albatross spends most of its life _____.
  a) on the ice   b) on land   c) at sea

4 The _____ is the largest animal that has ever lived on
  our planet.
  a) blue whale   b) great white shark   c) killer whale

5 Blue whales eat _____.
  a) killer whales   b) small animals   c) plants

6 Most of Greenland has _____ over it.
  a) roads   b) ice   c) trees

7 There are _____ under the Siberian Shelf.
  a) plants   b) people   c) minerals

Read Chapter 10. Answer the questions.

1 When did the first ocean travellers push their boats into
  the sea?

2 Why is it dark in the deep ocean?

3 What does the anglerfish have on its head?

4 What did Cornelius Drebbel build?

5 What did ships put on the floor of the Atlantic Ocean in
  1866?

6 How many new sea animals and plants did the
  Challenger find?

7 Who was the first person to travel to the bottom of the
  Challenger Deep?

ACTIVITIES

After Reading

1 **These two paragraphs are about two groups of ocean people. Complete the titles and the paragraphs using the words below.**

animals, Atlantic, Easter, faster, gold, islands, journeys, Lapita, narrow, navigate, Norway, Pacific, sea, stars, stealing, surprise, trade, Vikings, wider, year

THE _____

About 4,000 years ago, these people made long _____ across the open _____. They were looking for new _____, because they wanted to make new homes. They took food, water, _____, and plants with them. They understood the _____ and knew where to find them at different times of the _____. They learned to _____, and sailed to many places in the _____ Ocean, like Hawaii, _____ Island, and New Zealand.

THE _____

These people came from _____ and Denmark. About a thousand years ago, they sailed across the _____ Ocean to North America. They were famous for fighting, killing, and _____. Their long, _____ boats, called longships, were better and _____ than any other boats. Often they took villages by _____, arriving early in the morning. People had to pay them to go away – with _____. They also had bigger, _____ ships, and they travelled in these to _____ with people in other countries.

2 Use the clues below to complete this crossword with words from the book. Then find the hidden nine-letter word.

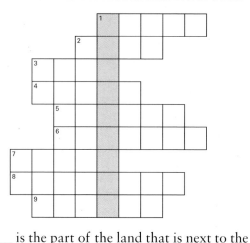

1 The _____ is the part of the land that is next to the sea.

2 The _____ is deep in the centre of the Earth.

3 The sea moves up and down every day because of the _____.

4 The water in our seas and oceans is _____.

5 Ferdinand Magellan was an important Portuguese _____.

6 The albatross has the _____ wings of any bird.

7 The blue _____ is the largest animal in the world.

8 The world's first telegraph cable went under the _____ Ocean.

9 Earth's crust is made of many tectonic _____.

The hidden word in the crossword is _____.
How many of these can you name?

3 Imagine you are Captain Bligh (see Chapter 8, *The open ocean*). You and your sailors have just arrived at Timor, in Indonesia. Write about what happened on *HMS Bounty*, and your journey to Timor. Start like this:

What a terrible journey! It all started about seven weeks ago. One night, while I was sleeping in my room,...

Use some of these words:

angry, boat, compass, guns, map, navigator, stars, thirsty

4 Read these sentences about problems with the oceans. Do you think they are true? What can we do about them?

1 The oceans are very big and deep, so we can put a lot of our rubbish in them.
2 It is good that the ice is melting more quickly, because it means that we can get more minerals from under the oceans.
3 We need to be more careful about the number of fish we catch, or one day they will all be gone.

5 Find out about Vasco da Gama, Christopher Columbus, Ferdinand Magellan, or John Cabot. Make a poster or give a talk to your class. Think about these questions:

• Where did they go?
• What were they looking for?
• What happened on their journeys?

ABOUT THE AUTHOR

Barnaby Newbolt has worked for many years as a teacher, a publisher, and an author of language teaching books. He has written two other titles for Oxford Bookworms Factfiles – *Climate Change* and *World Wonders* (both Stage 2).

He lives and works in Cornwall, in the far southwest of England, at the edge of the Atlantic Ocean.

'From my desk, I look south over the sea,' he says. 'The view is different every day: the sea is never the same from one day to the next. There is always something new to look at, and something new to learn.'

OXFORD BOOKWORMS LIBRARY

Classics • Crime & Mystery • Factfiles • Fantasy & Horror
Human Interest • Playscripts • Thriller & Adventure
True Stories • World Stories

The OXFORD BOOKWORMS LIBRARY provides enjoyable reading in English, with a wide range of classic and modern fiction, non-fiction, and plays. It includes original and adapted texts in seven carefully graded language stages, which take learners from beginner to advanced level. An overview is given on the next pages.

All Stage 1 titles are available as audio recordings, as well as over eighty other titles from Starter to Stage 6. All Starters and many titles at Stages 1 to 4 are specially recommended for younger learners. Every Bookworm is illustrated, and Starters and Factfiles have full-colour illustrations.

The OXFORD BOOKWORMS LIBRARY also offers extensive support. Each book contains an introduction to the story, notes about the author, a glossary, and activities. Additional resources include tests and worksheets, and answers for these and for the activities in the books. There is advice on running a class library, using audio recordings, and the many ways of using Oxford Bookworms in reading programmes. Resource materials are available on the website <www.oup.com/bookworms>.

The *Oxford Bookworms Collection* is a series for advanced learners. It consists of volumes of short stories by well-known authors, both classic and modern. Texts are not abridged or adapted in any way, but carefully selected to be accessible to the advanced student.

You can find details and a full list of titles in the *Oxford Bookworms Library Catalogue* and *Oxford English Language Teaching Catalogues*, and on the website <www.oup.com/bookworms>.

THE OXFORD BOOKWORMS LIBRARY
GRADING AND SAMPLE EXTRACTS

STARTER • 250 HEADWORDS

present simple – present continuous – imperative –
can/cannot, must – *going to* (future) – simple gerunds …

Her phone is ringing – but where is it?

Sally gets out of bed and looks in her bag. No phone. She looks under the bed. No phone. Then she looks behind the door. There is her phone. Sally picks up her phone and answers it. *Sally's Phone*

STAGE 1 • 400 HEADWORDS

… past simple – coordination with *and*, *but*, *or* –
subordination with *before*, *after*, *when*, *because*, *so* …

I knew him in Persia. He was a famous builder and I worked with him there. For a time I was his friend, but not for long. When he came to Paris, I came after him – I wanted to watch him. He was a very clever, very dangerous man. *The Phantom of the Opera*

STAGE 2 • 700 HEADWORDS

… present perfect – *will* (future) – *(don't) have to, must not, could* –
comparison of adjectives – simple *if* clauses – past continuous –
tag questions – *ask/tell* + infinitive …

While I was writing these words in my diary, I decided what to do. I must try to escape. I shall try to get down the wall outside. The window is high above the ground, but I have to try. I shall take some of the gold with me – if I escape, perhaps it will be helpful later. *Dracula*

STAGE 3 • 1000 HEADWORDS

... should, may – present perfect continuous – *used to* – past perfect –
causative – relative clauses – indirect statements ...

Of course, it was most important that no one should see
Colin, Mary, or Dickon entering the secret garden. So Colin
gave orders to the gardeners that they must all keep away
from that part of the garden in future. *The Secret Garden*

STAGE 4 • 1400 HEADWORDS

... past perfect continuous – passive (simple forms) –
would conditional clauses – indirect questions –
relatives with *where/when* – gerunds after prepositions/phrases ...

I was glad. Now Hyde could not show his face to the world
again. If he did, every honest man in London would be proud
to report him to the police. *Dr Jekyll and Mr Hyde*

STAGE 5 • 1800 HEADWORDS

... future continuous – future perfect –
passive (modals, continuous forms) –
would have conditional clauses – modals + perfect infinitive ...

If he had spoken Estella's name, I would have hit him. I was so
angry with him, and so depressed about my future, that I could
not eat the breakfast. Instead I went straight to the old house.
Great Expectations

STAGE 6 • 2500 HEADWORDS

... passive (infinitives, gerunds) – advanced modal meanings –
clauses of concession, condition

When I stepped up to the piano, I was confident. It was as if I
knew that the prodigy side of me really did exist. And when I
started to play, I was so caught up in how lovely I looked that
I didn't worry how I would sound. *The Joy Luck Club*

BOOKWORMS · FACTFILES · STAGE 2
Climate Change
BARNABY NEWBOLT

It's a terrible problem – or it's really not as bad as people say. There will be sudden big changes – or slower changes that we can learn to live with. It means the end for many animals, people, even whole islands – or the beginning for growing food in the Sahara.

What is the true story about climate change? Who is right – and what can we do about it? If we learn about the past, then perhaps there will be time to make changes for the future.

BOOKWORMS · FACTFILES · STAGE 3
The Everest Story

TIM VICARY

It is beautiful to look at, hard to reach, and terribly difficult to climb. Winds of 200 kilometres per hour or more scream across it day and night, while the temperature falls to -20 °C or lower. Every year, some who try to climb the highest mountain in the world do not return.

But for a century people have been coming to climb Everest – some alone, some in groups, but all with a dream of going to the highest place in the world. This is their story.